CONTENTS

TEACHER'S IMPLEMENTATION HANDBOOK

Reaching All Students

Students ... typically demonstrate diversity in the ways they best learn. It is important, therefore, that students have opportunities to learn in a variety of ways — individually, cooperatively, independently, with teacher direction, through hands-on experience, through examples followed by practice. The subject of mathematics varies in terms of the type of knowledge (concepts, skills, processes) that it contains, and competence in each type may be accomplished in different ways.

From *The Ontario Curriculum, Grades 9 and 10: Mathematics, 1999*

There are many reasons why different teaching approaches are necessary. These reasons include the following:

- Different students learn in different ways.
- Different curriculum expectations require different approaches.
- Concepts, as a rule, should be developed from the concrete to the abstract or symbolic, and the rate at which students move from the concrete to the abstract varies.
- Every class has exceptional students at both ends of the spectrum; adapting the instructional approach is one way to accommodate these students.
- A variety of approaches in a mathematics class keeps students and teachers engaged.
- Whole-class instruction, group work, and individual and independent learning are all important, and a balance of grouping strategies should be used.

Different Students Learn in Different Ways

There are many different learning style models. Some popular models include the division of auditory/visual/kinesthetic. Other models concern the organization of multiple intelligences: linguistic, musical, logical-mathematical, spatial, bodily-kinesthetic, and inter- and intra-personal. Students should not necessarily be categorized and separated according to learning styles because each student has a different balance of learning styles. Some teaching approaches will best reach some students, while other approaches might reach other students. For instance, a student who relates well visually rather than in an auditory or linguistic style would appreciate diagrams and charts as explanations to problems rather than just a verbal or written description of a solution. A student who learns kinesthetically works well with manipulatives or is eager to learn when he or she can move about in front of a motion detector to compare relations.

MATHPOWER 9 ™

ONTARIO EDITION

Teacher's Resource Binder

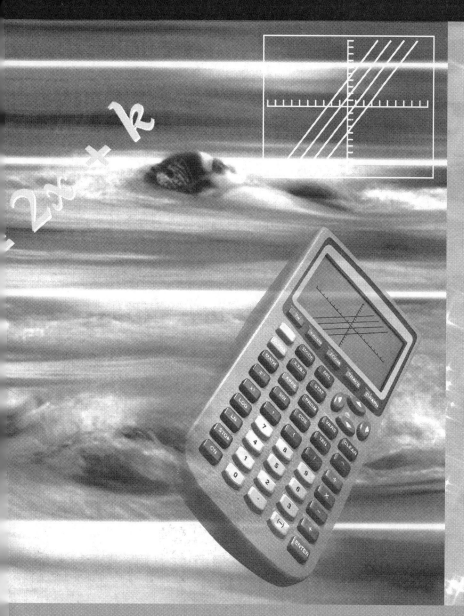

Teacher's Implementation Handbook

McGraw-Hill Ryerson

McGraw-Hill Ryerson Limited

A Subsidiary of The McGraw·Hill Companies

MATHPOWER™ 9, Ontario Edition
Teacher's Resource Binder

ISBN 0-07-560797-2

http://www.mcgrawhill.ca

1 2 3 4 5 6 7 8 9 0   MP   0 9 8 7 6 5 4 3 2 1 0

Printed and bound in Canada

Care has been taken to trace ownership of copyright material contained in this text. The publishers will gladly take any information that will enable them to rectify any reference or credit in subsequent printings.

Claris and ClarisWorks are registered trademarks of Claris Corporation.
Microsoft is a registered trademark of Microsoft Corporation.
The Geometer's Sketchpad® is a registered trademark of Key Curriculum Press, Inc.
Microsoft Excel and Microsoft Works are registered trademarks of Microsoft Corporation.
TI-GRAPH LINK™ is a registered trademark of Texas Instruments Incorporated.
Program-link™ is a registered trademark of CASIO Computer Co., Inc.
TI-92, TI-92 Plus, TI-83, TI-83 Plus are registered trademarks of Texas Instruments Incorporated.
CFX-9850 GB PLUS and EA-100 Data Analyzer are registered trademarks of CASIO Computer Co., Inc.
Windows® is a registered trademark of Microsoft Corporation.
Macintosh® is a registered trademark of Apple Computer, Inc.
Cabri Geometry II™ is a registered trademark of Université Joseph Fourier.
Calculator-Based Laboratory™, CBL™, and Calculator-Based Ranger™, CBR™ are registered trademarks of Texas Instruments Incorporated.

Canadian Cataloguing in Publication Data
Main entry under title:
Mathpower 9, Ontario edition. Teacher's resource binder
ISBN 0-07-560797-2
1 Mathematics — Study and teaching (Secondary).   I. Williams, Jackie C., date.
II. Title: Mathpower nine.
QA107.M37642 1999 Suppl. 2   510   C99-931657-5

PUBLISHERS: Diane Wyman, Carol Altilia
EDITORIAL CONSULTING: Michael J. Webb Consulting Inc.
ASSOCIATE EDITOR: Jean Ford
SENIOR SUPERVISING EDITOR: Carol Altilia
COPY EDITORS: Susan Marshall, Mary Agnes Challoner
PERMISSIONS EDITOR: Jacqueline Donovan
SENIOR PRODUCTION COORDINATOR: Yolanda Pigden
PRODUCTION COORDINATOR: Kay Badcock
INTERIOR DESIGN: ArtPlus Limited
ELECTRONIC PAGE MAKE-UP: ArtPlus Limited and Carlisle Communications, Ltd.
COVER DESIGN: Dianna Little
COVER ILLUSTRATIONS: Citrus Media
COVER IMAGE: ©Chris Amarol/Nonstock/PNI; ©Roy Bishop/Stock, Boston/PN

Different Curriculum Expectations Require Different Approaches

The specific expectations within the grade 9 curriculum relate to one or more of the four categories of the Achievement Chart. These different categories are best addressed in different ways.

If the expectation falls into the following Achievement Chart category:	the following approaches are suggested:
Knowledge/Understanding	Teacher-Directed Lesson Discovery Lesson Inquiry Model
Thinking/Inquiry/Problem Solving	Cooperative Learning Experiments Conjectures
Communication	Cooperative Learning Journals Portfolios Group Presentations
Application	Investigations Projects

Use a variety of teaching approaches and learning activities to address all expectations effectively. Even during one lesson, you might use several different approaches. Know your curriculum. Pay attention to the categories of each expectation and deliver your lesson appropriately.

> Not all students relate to one method of teaching. It is important to use a variety of approaches to teach the same concept. At least one approach will reach the individual student.

Moving From the Concrete to the Abstract

The use of manipulatives is essential when introducing new concepts. Students need to explore new concepts using concrete materials and a "hands-on" approach. When they have become familiar with a concept, they can be guided to develop an abstract model of the concept. Some students need to spend more time than others at the initial stages. For instance, when developing concepts in algebra using algebra tiles, you will find there are many students who are able to move quickly to the abstract model whereas some students will need to keep the algebra tiles at their desks a little bit longer before they move to diagrams of tiles and then finally to the abstract. Some students will need to return to the tiles for each new related skill or concept, while others will be able to incorporate the new learnings at an abstract level.

Exceptional Students

Exceptional students may require program modifications that specifically address their strengths and needs in learning mathematics.

From *The Ontario Curriculum, Grades 9 and 10: Mathematics, 1999*

All students should be given the opportunity to demonstrate their achievement at their best level of performance. Consider the following suggestions:

- Use a variety of teaching approaches.

- Provide enrichment and remediation opportunities.

- Recognize that students move at different paces, so allow extra time for students who need it and provide extension activities for students who move quickly through activities.

- Provide appropriate prompts to students who have difficulty with open-ended problems.

- Suggest or provide organizers (charts, tables) for students whose organizational skills are poorly developed. Help to develop their organizational skills so that they can eventually design their own organizers.

- Provide opportunities for students to demonstrate achievement at all four levels. Opportunities to demonstrate a level 4 performance need to be built into activities.

SOMETHING TO THINK ABOUT

Adults also prefer different types of instruction:
When you are given directions, do you prefer a map, a written list of directions, or are you able to remember oral directions?

Teachers also prefer different teaching approaches:
Do you prefer one approach over another? Have you thought about why? Do you vary teaching approaches deliberately or unintentionally?

Take a personal inventory of the approaches you have used in your math class over the past month or year. Is there room for improvement? How could you incorporate more approaches effectively?

Keep in mind that one approach to teaching mathematics does not serve all of the students all of the time no matter how well it is delivered.

Hands-On Learning in the High School Math Class

The philosophy of the grade 9 courses … reflects the belief that students learn mathematics effectively when they have initial opportunities to explore through hands-on experiences, followed by careful guidance into an understanding of the abstract mathematics involved.

From *The Ontario Curriculum, Grades 9 and 10: Mathematics, 1999*

What Is Hands-On Learning?

Students use manipulatives and tools in order to understand or solve a problem or to model and understand a mathematical concept.

WHY USE MANIPULATIVES AND TOOLS?	
Reason	**Example**
Manipulatives can be used to model mathematical concepts.	The impact of exponential growth can be appreciated if it is modelled using sequences of linking cube models: 1 (1 by 1 by 1), 8 (2 by 2 by 2), 27 (3 by 3 by 3), 64 (4 by 4 by 4), and so on.
Manipulatives and tools can be used to reach and engage different types of learners.	Some students, particularly tactile and visual learners, learn more effectively, and more willingly, when they can "handle" and "see" the math.
The sharing and use of manipulatives and tools in small groups requires cooperation, communication, and interaction.	If students in a group are provided square tiles to find the optimal rectangle, they have to work together to manipulate the tiles, giving each other directions and deciding how to record their discoveries. Sharing tools and manipulatives that are in short supply such as Miras encourages students to cooperate and interact.
Manipulatives can be used to introduce and explain procedures, algorithms, and formulas.	When students model algebraic expressions with algebra tiles, they can clearly see which terms are "like" terms in order to simplify the expressions. The algebraic terms x^2 and x do not look very different in an algebraic expression, but, as tiles, they are significantly different in size.
Manipulatives make it easier for students to communicate or talk about what they are doing, and to explain sophisticated mathematical concepts.	Students may not be able to use mathematical terminology to explain why a cube is the optimal rectangular prism, but they can use the language of the manipulatives, for example, "A cube uses the same number of cubes (*equal volume*), but it has the fewest faces on the outside (*least surface area*)."
Manipulatives link mathematics strands and explain mathematical language.	Numbers such as 8, 27, 64, and so on are "cubic" numbers because they form a cube when modelled. This idea links numeration and geometry and also number sense and spatial sense.
Manipulatives and tools provide opportunities for a different teaching approach and engage reluctant learners.	Many students will be enticed into learning new concepts if a novel approach is used. For example, compare 1) factoring polynomials using pencil-and-paper methods with 2) creating rectangular arrays of algebra tiles to represent the polynomial and then determining dimensions (factors).
Manipulatives and tools allow students to solve problems they could not solve otherwise and also allow students with a range of abilities to solve the same problem.	In order to determine if it is possible for an equilateral triangle to also be a right triangle, some students need to manipulate straws of equal length to represent the sides, but others can visualize the situation, while still others will be able to apply the Pythagorean Theorem.

Manipulatives and Tools in the *MATHPOWER™ 9, Ontario Edition,* Program

	Suggested Uses	**Example actvity from the MATHPOWER™ 9, Ontario Edition, Program Students:**
Linking Cubes	• Measurement (surface area and volume relationships) • Geometry (modelling rectangular prisms and irregular structures) • Numeration (powers, patterning, and ratio)	• look at patterns in surface area as cubes are added to a rectangular prism (Ch. 1). • create structures and then draw their isometric and orthographic views (Ch. 9).
Square Tiles*	• Measurement (area and perimeter relationships) • Numeration (powers and patterning) • Geometry (modelling rectangles and composite figures)	• relate the perimeter and area of different pentominoes (Ch. 9). • model square numbers using square arrays (Ch. 1).
Algebra Tiles* x-tile l-tile y-tile	• Algebra (simplifying expressions; adding, subtracting, multiplying, dividing, and factoring polynomials; solving equations) • Numeration (integers)	• model algebraic equations and then manipulate the tiles to model the process of solving an equation (Ch. 7). • use 1-tiles to model integer addition and subtraction (Ch. 1).
Geoboards*	• Measurement (perimeter and area relationships; the Pythagorean Theorem) • Numeration (fractions and decimals) • Analytic Geometry (slope)	• develop Pick's formula for area (Ch. 7). • model right triangles and compare the slopes of the hypotenuses (Ch. 8).
Miras	• Symmetry and Motion Geometry • Geometry (geometric constructions)	• draw angle bisectors, right bisectors, and perpendicular lines (Ch. 10).
Nets of 3-D Objects	• Measurement (surface area and volume; capacity and volume) • Geometry (relationships between 2-D and 3-D shapes)	• calculate surface area (Ch. 9). • develop formulas for the surface area of prisms, cylinders, cones, pyramids, and spheres (Ch. 9).

*Overhead manipulatives available.

Non-commercial manipulatives:

• Paper: for example, the expression $\left(\frac{1}{2}\right)^3$ or $\frac{1}{2} \times \frac{1}{2} \times \frac{1}{2}$ can be modelled by folding a piece of paper in half three times to get eight sections, each of which is $\frac{1}{8}$ of the paper.

• Toothpicks and straws can be used to represent polygon sides and diagonals.

Alternatives to manipulatives:

• Square dot paper can be used instead of geoboards. Students can also use dot paper to record their geoboard constructions.

• Grid paper can be used instead of square tiles (and to record constructions).

• Algebra tile blackline masters can be used instead of the actual tiles.

Cooperative Learning

When students work in pairs or in small groups, there are "low stakes" opportunities for students to try out their own tentative ideas and to listen to the reactions and ideas of a small number of classmates. Appropriately structured interactions can help students learn to listen and express their mathematical ideas clearly.

From *NCTM Principles and Standards for School Mathematics:*
Discussion Draft, October 1998

What Is Cooperative Learning?

Effective cooperative learning opportunities have the following three characteristics:

Interdependence   **Individual accountability**   **Interaction**

Students work together *interdependently* (the task cannot be completed unless each group member does his or her part) with *individual accountability* (each group member adopts a specific role or task) while *interacting* (assisting, discussing, and offering support and encouragement).

Instructional Benefits of Cooperative Learning

Effective cooperative learning provides

- opportunities for **communication** among students and between students and teachers
- a **safe, non-threatening environment** so that students can take risks
- a **practical solution to a shortage of materials** such as calculators and manipulatives
- opportunities for students to develop **leadership skills**
- **opportunities for peer tutoring,** as required
- **opportunity for assessment:** teachers can observe and conduct informal interviews
- **another instructional approach,** for example, alternating cooperative learning with direct instruction in the same lesson keeps students engaged
- the most **practical and effective forum for meeting certain curriculum expectations,** for example, RE1.03 (collect data, using appropriate equipment and/or technology) and MG3.04 (pose questions about geometric relationships, and communicate the findings, using appropriate language and mathematical forms)
- an opportunity for students to **prepare for formal** group and class **presentations**

Management Suggestions for Effective Cooperative Learning

- Pairs and groups of three or four students is preferable, although larger groups will be necessary for certain purposes.
- Use cooperative learning appropriately: there are certain activities that are more effective when students work on their own; some are more effective when students work in groups.
- Use cooperative learning strategies appropriately: some strategies suit certain activities.
- Use a variety of cooperative learning strategies.
- Build in individual accountability; for example, each student is assigned a specific role or task, or each student must submit a written summary or solution.
- Build in interdependence so that each group member must do his or her part to complete the task.
- Teach cooperative learning skills explicitly and implicitly. Work with students to develop their skills for working in groups; use Assessment Master 2 in the Assessment and Evaluation Handbook as a guide.
- Allow groups time to develop a working rapport but be prepared to change and adjust groups as often as necessary, for variety and for more effective student combinations.

Reasons for Cooperative Learning

Task completion   Problem solving   Discussion
Practice/drill   Peer teaching   Homework check
Investigations/experiments   Share materials   Projects

Types of Groups	Reasons for Grouping
Self-selected	Particularly useful when there is a great deal of work to be done outside the classroom
Proximity	Quick grouping for unexpected or impromptu cooperative learning opportunities
Student "personalities"	Combining students to ensure they work effectively
Student interest	For student-chosen contexts or problems
Heterogeneous by ability	Any activity where it is beneficial to combine weak, average, and strong students
Homogeneous by ability	To deliver remedial and enrichment activities

A Sample of Cooperative Learning Strategies

Pairs Share Students work together in pairs to solve a problem. Each pair meets with another pair to discuss, compare, and check solutions.	**Pairs Drill** Students work in pairs on practice questions: one partner does odd questions while the other does even. The partners then exchange and check each other's solutions.
Brainstorm Students work in small groups to brainstorm ideas in response to an open-ended question, problem, or topic. All ideas are recorded, and then the group refines the list and chooses the best two or three ideas to share with the class.	**Numbered Heads** Students in small groups are each assigned a number. The groups discuss, solve a problem, or answer a question. The teacher then picks a random number, and students in each group with that number report to the class.
Roundtable The teacher asks a question or poses a problem. Students in small groups take turns recording one response or one step in the solution and then pass the paper to the next group member.	**Cooperative Review** Students in pairs or groups create a problem or question and then exchange with another group to solve. The solutions are passed back to the original group for checking.
Jigsaw Each student in a home group is assigned a topic, skill, or strategy to learn. They work in expert groups to learn about the topic, or master the skill or strategy, returning to their home group to inform or teach group members.	**Pairs Check** A group of four divides into two pairs. In each pair, one student does question 1, while the partner acts as coach. The partners then switch roles for question 2. The group of four then reconvenes to discuss and check solutions.
Think-Pair-Share The teacher asks a question. Each student thinks about a response, then shares his or her answers with a partner. Students then share their answers with the class.	**Consensus** Students work in small groups to discuss a topic, question, or problem. The group must reach a consensus about, and report on, the best response to a problem or solution to the problem.

NOTE: Some strategies are more suitable than others for certain activities or problems. Build a repertoire of cooperative learning strategies and allow students to select strategies that they feel would be most effective.

Mathematical Modelling and the Inquiry Process

What Is Mathematical Modelling?

An important stage in the inquiry process is that of mathematical modelling, or taking the conditions of a real-life situation and describing them in mathematical form. A mathematical model can appear in many different ways — as an actual physical model, or as a diagram, a graph, a table of values, an equation, or a computer model.

From *The Ontario Curriculum, Grades 9 and 10: Mathematics, 199*

You do it all the time and so do your students. You take in information, or data, from the real world and you reshape it or model it in a form that you can understand and use. For example, someone gives you directions over the phone. You may write them down or you might draw a map that models the same information but in a form with which you feel more comfortable. As you look at the map, you notice relationships, for example, the last road you drew for your route is perpendicular to the street you live on. You might also notice discrepancies that were not apparent in the oral directions that need to be addressed — perhaps the directions are incorrect.

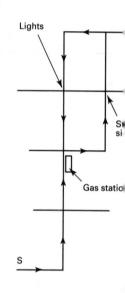

Modelling in mathematics serves the same purpose as drawing the map. Mathematical modelling is a form of problem solving, an integral part of the inquiry process.

Why Should We Focus Attention on Mathematical Modelling

One of our ultimate goals as teachers is to prepare young people to function confidently and knowledgeably in real-world situations. Mathematical modeling is a form of real-world problem solving. ... A modeling approach to problem solving focuses a variety of mathematical skills on finding a solution and helps students see mathematics in a broad spectrum of applications.

From NCTM *Mathematical Modeling in the Secondary School Curriculum, 199*

Mathematical modelling ...

- allows students to "see" patterns and relationships. For example, the pattern in the numbers 1, 3, 6, 10, ... is not readily apparent to many students, but, if it is modelled with counters, the pattern +2, +3, +4, ... becomes more apparent. The relationship between numeration and geometry also becomes apparent. As well, mathematical language can often be explained through models — 10 is a "triangular number" because, when modelled geometrically, it forms a triangle.

      · 1

      ∴ 3

      ∴∴ 6

      ∴∴∴ 1(

- is a way to solve problems. Numerical and algebraic expressions, graphs, geometric models, equations and formulas, and tables of values are all different types of models. They serve different purposes but all play a role in solving problems. In rich problem solving situations, students use multiple models to solve problems.

- provides forms in which to communicate solutions to problems. Students can represent their discoveries and results using tables of values, graphs, diagrams, physical models, and/or formulas and equations.

Mathematical Modelling and the Curriculum

Many of the expectations in the grade 9 curriculum require students to use and become proficient at mathematical modelling. For example:

- Use algebraic modelling as one of several problem solving strategies.
- Organize and analyze data using appropriate techniques.
- Communicate solutions to problems in appropriate mathematical forms.
- Construct tables of values, graphs, scatter plots, lines of best fit, and formulas.

Mathematical Modelling in *MATHPOWER™ 9, Ontario Edition*, Student Text

Ch.	In order to solve problems in this chapter, students . . .	In the *Modelling Math* section at the end of this chapter, students . . .
1	work with numerical and algebraic models.	interpret data that is modelled in tables of values in order to create scale drawings to model astronomical relationships.
2	work with numerical models.	interpret and manipulate data about the environment that is modelled in a table of values and a map.
3	work with numerical models.	interpret and manipulate data that is modelled in a map in order to solve transportation problems.
4	model data using measures of central tendency, and a variety of statistical plots and graphs.	collect and then model data about word use in a graph in order to identify patterns in word usage by different authors and in different subject areas.
5	model relationships as ordered pairs, graphs, and equations.	interpret sports data modelled in a graph in order to look for trends.
6	work with algebraic models.	collect data from a sample of reading material and then model it in a numerical score in order to compare reading level difficulty in different excerpts.
7	use algebraic modelling.	model information about fingerprints in a formula used to classify fingerprints.
8	model problem situations using graphs and equations.	interpret information modelled in a topographical map to solve related problems. They also model the relationship between altitude and distance in a graph.
9	apply and create measurement formulas (mathematical models). They also create tables of values in order to explore relationships.	investigate different models of map projections and solve related problems, for example, determine location by latitude and longitude and calculate the surface area and circumference of the Earth.
10	create computer models or draw geometric diagrams in order to determine geometric relationships.	model their peripheral vision by measuring it and representing it as an angle measurement. They apply their model of peripheral vision to evaluate peripheral vision standards for certain types of helmets.

Communication in Mathematics

The importance of communication in mathematics is a highlight of the elementary school curriculum and continues to be a highlight in secondary school. ... This curriculum assumes a classroom environment in which students are called upon to explain their reasoning in writing, or orally to the teacher, to the class, or to other students in a group.

From *The Ontario Curriculum, Grades 9 and 10: Mathematics, 1999*

What Communication in Mathematics Means

Students should learn the language and symbolism of mathematics to communicate mathematical ideas in order to

- express mathematical ideas orally and in writing
- read and understand written presentations of mathematics
- construct an understanding of mathematical concepts by having to explain them
- reflect on and clarify their own thinking about mathematical concepts
- express patterns/relationships discovered through exploration and investigation and formulate mathematical definitions and generalizations
- use clear language in order to ask questions about mathematical concepts
- recognize the global value of mathematical notation and its role in the development and sharing of mathematical ideas

How Students Develop Communication in Mathematics

Communication in mathematics is developed by giving students various opportunities for listening, speaking, writing, reading, and presenting. Group work specifically encourages discussion, questioning, active listening, and reporting. Journal writing and presentations provide the opportunity for summarizing and explaining. It is often not enough for students to write the answer or "show all their steps." They also need opportunities to explain how they obtained the solution, what other methods they tried, their stumbling blocks, and at what moment they clearly saw how to arrive at the solution.

Communication Is Linked to Specific and Overall Expectations

Communication is one of the four categories of the Achievement Chart and thus must be included in the assessment of many of the specific and overall expectations. Several expectations relate specifically to communication. They are easily identified because they contain words such as "describe," "communicate," or "explain." Pay particular attention to the wording of each expectation: if it involves communication, then the student's ability to communicate must be assessed in addition to the other categories associated with that expectation, that is, Knowledge/Understanding, Application, and/or Thinking/Inquiry/Problem Solving.

For example:

- "communicate" solutions to problems in appropriate mathematics forms and "justify" the reasoning used in solving the problems
- "describe" the connections between various representations of relations
- "pose" problems, "identify" variables, and "formulate" hypotheses associated with relationships
- "explain" the significance of optimal surface area or volume in various applications

Forms of Communication

Form	Description, Purpose, and Management Tips
Oral presentations . . .	provide students with the opportunity to explain their solutions and strategies to their peers in a class presentation or to a small group. Teachers can encourage thoughtful presentations by asking different groups to present different aspects of the solution such as: • What was the most difficult part in solving this problem? • How did each member of the group contribute to the solution of the problem? • If a group could not find the solution to a problem, what would you suggest to them?
Math journals . . .	encourage students to articulate ideas, to reflect on their learnings, to summarize and extend topics, and to express their feelings about math.
Portfolios . . .	• consist of students' work and reflections about the work that they have chosen to include in the portfolio or that the teacher has chosen to include. • demonstrate growth, or lack of growth. There are different types of portfolios. For example: • Problem Solving Portfolios • Demonstration of Achievement of Expectations Portfolios • Project Portfolios • Attitudes About Learning/Reflective Portfolios
Cooperative learning . . .	provides an opportunity for students to develop mathematical concepts through explaining and listening to others. For example: • Jigsaw Strategy (expert group members teach their home group members) • Pairs Share Strategy (one student teaches the other how to do the first question, they switch roles for the second question, and so on)
Written submissions . . .	provide an opportunity for students to explain, in writing: • the solution to a problem, including the reasoning used in solving the problem • a description of the stumbling blocks and how they were overcome • strategies that were tried but did not work or had to be adapted
Open-ended questions . . .	can be used in all aspects of teaching and learning. Some sample leading open-ended questions are: • Is this always true? Can you prove it? • What would happen if . . . ? • Convince me that you know how to . . . ?
Conferences and interviews . . .	• can be conducted with individuals, pairs, or small groups. • can be informal, as students are working, or formal, upon completion of a project, to accompany a portfolio submission, or to discuss progress reports. Teachers should prepare a list of basic questions, designed to help assess expectations. These questions, of course, will evolve as the interview progresses. The teacher should record anecdotal remarks to refer to at a later date when assessing student achievement.

Learning About Problem Solving

In order to become successful problem solvers, students need opportunities to examine and apply a variety of problem solving strategies. George Polya's four-step problem solving model is presented at the beginning of the *MATHPOWER™ 9, Ontario Edition*, student text and is revisited in each of the first four chapters in the Problem Solving feature sections. Twelve problem solving strategies are presented in the first four chapters. In each section, students are shown an example of how a problem can be solved using the focus strategy. Students can then apply the focus strategy, and/or other strategies, to solve a variety of problems on the accompanying Applications and Problem Solving page.

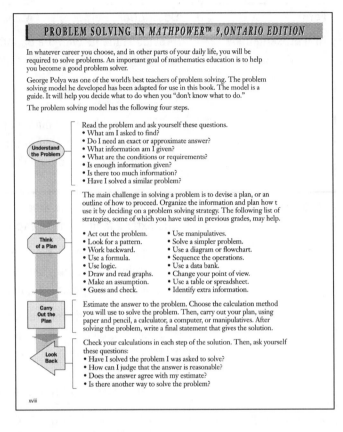

Why Teach "About" Problem Solving

Students build a repertoire of problem solving strategies. Students can use these strategies at any stage in the model, for example, they may need to draw a diagram to Understand the Problem (Step 1) and then look for a pattern to Think of a Plan and Carry It Out (Steps 2 and 3). To Look Back (Step 4), a student might use an alternative strategy to check his or her solution. In more complex and rich problem solving situations, students will need to combine strategies. For example, they might draw a diagram to generate data, organize the data in a table, and then guess and check. It is important to keep in mind that, although there are students who seem to intuitively develop and apply problem solving strategies where appropriate, there are many who require more deliberate instruction.

Students learn the language of problem solving: As in all areas of mathematics, communication is increasingly emphasized. Providing students with the appropriate terminology will assist them in thinking, talking, and writing about problem solving.

Students have a generic problem solving model to use, or depart from, as necessary: As students work through the problem solving process, they learn to ask themselves standard questions such as "What am I asked to find?" and "What information am I given?" One of the standard questions in the Look Back step — "How can I judge that the answer is reasonable?" — is a prompt for students to judge the reasonableness of their answers as required by the curriculum (specific expectations NA1.05, NA1.06, and MG2.04).

The four-step problem solving model also provides a model for presenting solutions. Students will find this model helpful in communicating their own solutions, either in writing or orally. On the first page of each Problem Solving section, students are shown an example of how the solution to a problem can be presented or communicated. This is particularly important for expectations where students are required to communicate solutions to problems in proper mathematical forms (NA4.03, RE1.06, and AG3.05).

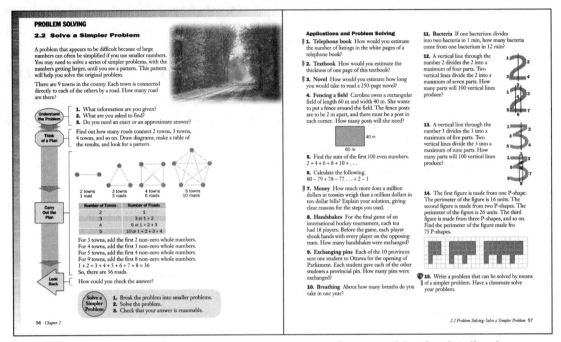

Sample Problem and Solution   **Opportunities for Application**

Using the Problem Solving Sections Effectively

It is always preferable for students to, at least, attempt to solve a problem before presenting them with a sample solution. In this way, the sample solution is more meaningful because the student has struggled with the problem and, in doing so, becomes familiar with it. Perhaps they have solved the problem in the same way, in a similar way, or in an entirely different way. For this reason, teachers should present the sample problem on the first page of a Problem Solving section to the class, while students' texts are closed. The problem can then be solved, either as a class, or with students in small groups or pairs. Do not force the solution to match the solution in the student text — if students take an entirely different yet reasonable direction, this should be encouraged. After students have solved the problem, they can open their texts and compare their solutions with the one shown on the student text page. Selected Applications and Problem Solving problems can then be either assigned, or selected by students.

Applying the Problem Solving Model and Strategies

It is expected that what students learn from these problem solving sections will be applied to all problem solving opportunities throughout the *MATHPOWER™ 9, Ontario Edition,* program whether they be simple one- or two-step problems or rich problem solving situations.

Rich Problem Solving Situations

Mathematical knowledge becomes meaningful and powerful in application. This curriculum embeds the learning of mathematics in the solving of problems based on real-life situations. Other disciplines are a ready source of effective contexts for the study of mathematics. Rich problem solving situations can be drawn from closely related disciplines, such as computer science, physics, or technology, as well as from subjects historically thought of as distant from mathematics, such as geography or art.

From *The Ontario Curriculum, Grades 9 and 10: Mathematics, 1999*

Characteristics of a Rich Problem Solving Situation

A rich problem solving situation has several of the following attributes:

- open-ended, leading to several possible solutions, strategies, or answers
- complex, engaging, and challenging
- set in a meaningful, "real-world" context
- an integration of several mathematics strands
- an application of mathematics to other disciplines, or an integration of disciplines
- a holistic approach to the categories of the Achievement Chart, that is, more than one category is addressed (Knowledge/Understanding, Communication, Thinking/Inquiry/Problem Solving, and Application)
- an emphasis on process and application

Purpose and Instructional Benefit of Rich Problem Solving Situations

Rich problem solving situations give students the opportunity to:

- see the usefulness of the math — math becomes a tool rather than a chore
- come to a deeper understanding of mathematical concepts
- make connections between different mathematical concepts and strands, between mathematics and other disciplines, and between mathematics and their world
- see the "big picture" of mathematics
- answer their own questions about "Where will we use this?"
- develop verbal and written communication skills
- be creative and express their own individuality
- develop a level of comfort with mathematics by reducing "math phobia"

Rich Problem Solving in the *MATHPOWER*™ *9, Ontario Edition,* Program

Students will find many rich problem solving situations in their textbook: the Logic, Pattern, Number, and Word Power problems at the end of selected sections, the Exploring Math column near the end of each chapter, the Computer Data Bank sections, the Career Connection sections, and the Applications and Problem Solving problems in each section.

Teachers are also directed to the Rich Learning Activities in the *MATHPOWER*™ *9, Ontario Edition, Blackline Masters.* Teachers are provided with a summary, the activity, suggested timing, student description, pedagogical context, instructional setting, expected observations, and, where appropriate, rubrics for assessment. There are also exemplars of student work provided for two of the activities. Information about where each Rich Learning Activity fits with respect to the *MATHPOWER*™ *9, Ontario Edition,* student text is also provided.

Some of the Rich Learning Activities are designed to introduce a topic in mathematics, for example, *Catch the Beat,* can be used to introduce a unit on analytic geometry; while others are designed to consolidate, for example, *An Interior Design Project* can be used to consolidate a grade 9 measurement unit.

A sample of one Rich Learning Activity follows:

The Present Problem

You will be provided with an irregular object. In your group, design a package to contain the object, while matching the shape as closely as possible. Make a net of the package. It can be life-size or a scale drawing with appropriate dimensions. Support your decision with numerical calculations. Report any considerations that led to your decision.

Expectations (Applied expectations are in parentheses.)
Knowledge/Understanding: NA3.06, MG2.02 (NA4.01, MG2.02)
Thinking/Inquiry/Problem Solving: NA1.05, MG2.01, MG2.02, MG2.03, MG2.04 (NA1.05, MG2.01, MG2.03, MG2.04, MG2.05)
Communication: NA4.03, MG1.03, MG3.04 (NA4.03, MG1.04, MG3.04)
Application: MGV.02, NA1.01, NA3.06 (MGV.02, NA1.02, NA3.05)

After working with the Rich Learning Activities and becoming familiar with their structure, teachers may want to create their own rich problem solving situations.

Creating a Rich Problem Solving Situation

Teachers are encouraged to work together with their colleagues to create rich problem solving situations. The task first begins with some creative brainstorming. *Do you first develop the activity and then choose expectations or do you begin with the expectations and then develop the activity?* The answer is yes to both questions. However, the expectations that are being addressed need to be constantly brought into focus. Students can often help in creating rich problem solving situations, particularly in providing relevant contexts. Students know their interests, and they also have a depth of experience in areas that perhaps the teacher does not, for example, sports statistics and technology. Frequently, a teacher can bring a starting point or idea into the class and the class can brainstorm and add other components — this is the richness. Students in higher grades can help to create activities for younger students.

Use the list of attributes found in *Characteristics of a Rich Problem Solving Situation* on page 16 of this handbook as a checklist to determine if you have, in fact, created a truly rich problem solving situation for your students. If your activity has at least three of the attributes, it probably qualifies as a rich problem solving situation.

Assessment of a Rich Problem Solving Situation

A rich problem solving situation is an opportunity for students to explore and investigate. However, teachers may also want to use some rich problem solving situations as opportunities for assessment, especially in the categories of Thinking/ Inquiry/Problem Solving, Communication, and Application. Performance in a rich problem solving situation is best assessed using rubrics, coupled with observation, and self- and peer-assessment. A more complete description of the assessment of a rich problem solving situation is provided in the *MATHPOWER™ 9, Ontario Edition, Teacher's Resource Binder*, Assessment and Evaluation Handbook.

Note that a complete assessment package accompanies some of the rich problem solving situations provided in the *MATHPOWER™ 9 Ontario Edition*, program (see the *MATHPOWER™ 9, Ontario Edition, Blackline Masters*, Rich Learning Activities).

Overview of Technology in *MATHPOWER*™ *9, Ontario Edition*, Student Text

The development of sophisticated yet easily used calculators and computers is changing the role of procedure and technique in mathematics. Operations that have been an essential part of a procedures-focused curriculum for decades can now be accomplished quickly and effectively using technology, so that students can now solve problems that were previously too time consuming to attempt, and can focus on underlying concepts.

From *The Ontario Curriculum, Grades 9 and 10: Mathematics, 1999*

Instructional Benefit of Using Technology

Technology ...

- **saves time,** for example, by reducing lengthy perimeter and area calculations, students can focus on the relationship between perimeter and area.
- **is a teaching tool,** for example, by graphing families of lines with different slopes, students will immediately see the effect on the steepness of the graph.
- **motivates and engages students,** for example, the use of scientific probes to collect real data will entice reluctant learners to get involved.
- **allows students to quickly check solutions to problems.**
- **allows investigations into areas of mathematics and contexts which would otherwise be inaccessible,** for example, the use of scientific probes to collect data about the rebound height of a ball.
- **demonstrates the connection between mathematics and other disciplines,** for example, by graphing and then displaying families of lines on a graphing calculator, students can see how mathematics applies to animation.

Appropriate Use of Technology

The presence of technology ... places an increasing importance on the ability of the students to make mental judgments about expected results.

From *The Ontario Curriculum, Grades 9 and 10: Mathematics, 1999*

The *MATHPOWER*™ *9, Ontario Edition*, program promotes the appropriate use of technology by providing technology activities as required and recommended by the new curriculum. Mathematical skills are still to be taught by the teacher and mastered by the student, but they are no longer the focus. Rather, problem solving and the application of skills in a wide variety of contexts is the focus.

Note that some of the expectations in the curriculum cannot be addressed without technology, for example, "graph lines, using graphing calculators or graphing software;" others are addressed best, at least in part, using technology, for example, "determine through investigation, the characteristics that distinguish the equation of a straight line from the equation of non-linear relations;" while the use of technology provides an additional, novel approach to extend or enhance other expectations, for example, "determine the meaning of negative exponents and of zero as an exponent, from activities using patterning."

The use of technology should extend students' understanding of the concepts rather than simply provide a shortcut. *MATHPOWER*™ *9, Ontario Edition*, program's emphasis on communication and estimation ensures that students demonstrate an understanding of mathematics and not just an ability to operate a computer or calculator.

Technology in the *MATHPOWER™ 9, Ontario Edition,* Student Text

NOTES:

1. An asterisk indicates that a scientific calculator could also be used.
2. Chapter references indicate where the application *first* appears in the textbook.
3. Expectation codes refer to the Academic curriculum. Expectation codes in brackets refer to the Applied curriculum.

Students use graphing calculators to . . .	Expectations, Applications, and Elaboration
evaluate expressions involving powers.* (Ch. 1)	NAV.02, NA2.01, NA2.02, NA2.03, NA2.05, NA2.06 (NAV.02, NA2.01, NA2.02, NA2.03, NA2.05, NA2.06) The graphing calculator allows the user to examine the entire expression, not just the last keystroke, while the user is entering the expression. As well, students use the calculator as a tool to develop the power rules.
generate* and sort random numbers. (Ch. 1)	RE1.02 (RE1.02) Students generate a list of random numbers given a range and number of numbers. This skill will be required in Chapter 4 Statistics for selecting random samples. The Sort Ascending instruction will be used to order data in order to determine median and mode.
evaluate expressions involving rational numbers.* (Ch. 1)	NA1.01, NA1.02 (NA1.03) Using the calculator allows students to move past their difficulties in manipulating complex expressions with decimals, integers, and fractions, unencumbered by the order of operations. NOTE: Students are expected to always estimate to check calculated answers.
evaluate expressions involving scientific notation.* (Ch. 3)	NA2.04, NA2.05 (NA2.04, NA2.05) Students change numbers in standard form to scientific notation and vice versa. They also calculate with numbers in scientific notation.
convert fractions to decimals* and decimals to fractions. (Ch. 3)	NAV.01, NA1.01, NA1.02, NA1.04 (NAV.01, NA1.03, NA1.04) Students • calculate with fractions, and then convert the final answer to fraction form; • compare fractions by converting them to decimals; and • use the calculator as a tool to determine the relationship between fractions and repeating decimals.

Students use graphing calculators to ...	Expectations, Applications, and Elaboration
evaluate expressions with square roots.* (Ch. 3)	NAV.01, NA1.02, NA1.04 (NAV.01, NA1.04) This skill will be required in later chapters for evaluating formulas involving squares and square roots, for example, the Pythagorean Theorem.
determine measures of central tendency: mean*, median, and mode. (Ch. 4)	RE1.04 (RE1.04) Students store the data in a list and then find all three averages by manipulating the list. To determine the mode, the list is sorted in ascending or descending order.
draw statistical graphs. (Ch. 4)	REV.01, RE1.04, RE1.06 (REV.01, RE1.04, RE1.06) Box-and-whisker plots, scatter plots, broken-line graphs, and histograms can be quickly created, manipulated, and interpreted using the STATS PLOT menu.
find the line of best fit. (Ch. 4)	REV.01, RE2.03 (REV.01, RE2.03) The line of best fit is first found by trial and error. Then, the Linear Regression instruction is used to find the most appropriate line of best fit.
collect, store, and organize data. (Ch. 4)	REV.01, RE1.03, RE1.04, RE1.06 (REV.01, RE1.03, RE1.04, RE1.06) Data collected from scientific probes or data from other secondary sources, such as Statistics Canada, can be stored in the graphing calculator as lists. Students can then manipulate the lists to create tables and graphs and to determine measures of central tendency.
plot points from a table of values to graph linear relations. (Ch. 5)	RE1.04, RE2.01, RE2.02, AG3.01, AG3.03 (RE1.04, RE2.01, RE2.02, AG3.01, AG3.03) Students enter tables of values as lists, create statistical plots, and then draw graphs using the Linear Regression instruction. Properties of linear relations can be developed easily as graphs are produced quickly.
graph linear and non-linear relations from equations. (Ch. 5)	RE1.04, RE2.01, RE2.04, AG3.03 (RE1.04, RE2.01, RE2.04, AG3.03) Students enter the equation directly into the graphing calculator and then create the graph with one keystroke. Properties of linear and non-linear relations can be developed quickly and easily as graphs are produced effortlessly.
interpolate and extrapolate from a graph. (Ch. 5)	RE3.01, AG3.06 (RE3.01) Students trace (Trace instruction) and zoom (Zoom instruction) and use the Value operation to determine the coordinates of points along graphs.

Technology in the *MATHPOWER*™ *9, Ontario Edition*, Student Text [Continued]

Students use graphing calculators to ...	Expectations, Applications, and Elaboration
find the equation of a line of best fit. (Ch. 5)	**RE2.03 (RE2.03)** Students first determine the equation by informal methods and then use the Linear Regression instruction to determine the equation.
develop the concepts of domain and range. (Ch. 5)	**RE1.04, RE2.01, RE2.04 (RE1.04, RE2.01, RE2.04)** When graphing equations, students adjust the window settings so that the graph appears in the display. In doing so, they are developing the concepts of domain and range.
add, subtract, multiply, divide, expand, factor, and evaluate polynomials. (Ch. 6)	**NA2.02, NAV.03, NA3.01, NA3.02, NA3.03 (NA2.02, NAV.03, NA3.01, NA3.02)** After learning the pencil-and-paper methods, students use a special graphing calculator to work with polynomials.
solve first-degree equations and rearrange equations. (Ch. 7)	**NAV.03, NA3.04, NA3.06 (NAV.03, NA3.03, NA3.06)** After learning the pencil-and-paper methods, students use a graphing calculator to solve first-degree equations and rearrange equations/formulas.
find the slope of a line given two points on the line. (Ch. 8)	**AG2.01** Students examine, enter, and then use a graphing calculator program for calculating slope that is based on the formula $m = \dfrac{y_2 - y_1}{x_2 - x_1}$.
determine characteristics of linear and non-linear equations. (Ch. 8)	**AGV.01, AG1.01, AG1.02 (AGV.01, AG1.01, AG1.02)** Students quickly graph equations, compare the shape of the graphs, and then match each equation with a straight-line graph or with a curved graph. They can then determine the characteristics that distinguish the equation of a linear relation from that of a non-linear relation.
determine the equation, the *y*-intercept, and the slope of a line given two points. (Ch. 8)	**AG3.01, AG3.03, AG3.04 (AG3.01, AG3.03, AG3.04)** Students enter the values of two points into the graphing calculator and then use the Linear Regression instruction to determine the equation of the line, in the form $y = mx + b$, that passes through the two points.

Students use graphing calculators to ...	Expectations, Applications, and Elaboration
discover the significance of the *y*-intercept and the slope in the equation $y = mx + b$. (Ch. 8)	AGV.02, AG3.03, AG3.04, AG3.06 (AGV.02, AG3.03, AG3.04) Students quickly graph families of lines and determine how changing the values of *b* (the *y*-intercept) and/or *m* (the slope) affects the appearance of a graph.
find the point of intersection of two lines. (Ch. 8)	AG3.08 Students quickly graph systems of equations, and then use the Intersect operation to find the point of intersection in four simple keystrokes.
distinguish between exact and approximate representations for surface area and volume of cylinders, cones, and spheres.* (Ch. 8)	NA1.02, MG2.01 Students express the exact surface area and volume of cylinders, cones, and spheres using the π symbol, and then calculate the approximate area using the π key and then rounding to a specified level of accuracy.
calculate surface area and volume.* (Ch. 8)	MG2.01 (MG2.02) In addition to using calculators to substitute into and evaluate measurement formulas, students examine, create, and then use graphing calculator programs to calculate surface area and volume.
Students use geometry software to ...	Expectations, Applications, and Elaboration
	NOTE: Geometry software allows for quick and accurate construction so students can focus on the expectations rather than be concerned about, and distracted by, the details of construction and the potential inaccuracies in construction and measuring.
determine the properties of interior and exterior angles of triangles and quadrilaterals. (Ch. 10)	MGV.03, MG3.01 (MGV.03, MG3.01)
construct medians, angle bisectors, altitudes, incircles, circumcircles, and centroids of triangles, and determine their properties. (Ch. 10)	MGV.03, MG3.02 (MGV.03, MG3.02)

Students use geometry software to ...	Expectations, Applications, and Elaboration
construct polygons and diagonals and investigate the properties of their sides and diagonals. (Ch. 10)	MGV.03, MG3.03 (MGV.03, MG3.03)
construct parallel lines and transversals and determine the properties of the resulting angles. (Ch. 10)	MGV.03, MG3.01 (MGV.03, MG3.01)
test conjectures about geometric relationships (Ch. 10)	MGV.03, MG3.04, MG3.05

Students use the Internet and computer data banks to ...	Expectations, Applications, and Elaboration
collect first- and second-hand data (throughout the student text and specifically in the Computer Data Bank sections).	REV.01, RE1.03 (REV.01, RE1.03) Students are prompted throughout the textbook and specifically in the Computer Data Bank sections to collect data in order to solve problems about a variety of topics such as the geography of Canada and food and nutrition using Internet data banks and the *MATHPOWER*™ *9, Ontario Edition, Computer Data Bank.*

Students use spreadsheets to ...	Expectations, Applications, and Elaboration
solve complex numerical problems. (Ch. 2)	NAV.01, NA1.03 Students organize and manipulate data in order to solve problems that would otherwise be tedious with many potential calculation errors.
display numerical data in a variety of creative graphs. (Ch. 4)	RE1.04, RE1.06 (RE1.04, RE1.06) Students use the chart feature, and their creativity to display data that they collect and organize in a spreadsheet. They create bar graphs, broken-line graphs, and circle graphs.

Students use spreadsheets to ...	Expectations, Applications, and Elaboration
create a scatter plot and draw a line of best fit. (Ch. 4)	REV.01, RE1.04, RE1.05, RE1.06, RE2.02, RE2.03 (REV.01, RE1.04, RE1.05, RE1.06, RE2.02, RE2.03) Students enter second-hand data and data collected from an experiment into spreadsheets, use the chart feature to create scatter plots, draw a line of best fit using the software (if this function is available), and then look for relationships.
investigate the relationship between perimeter and area. (Ch. 9)	MGV.01, MG1.04 (MGV.01, MG1.01) Students use the special capabilities of a spreadsheet to automatically recalculate measurements to determine a minimum perimeter for a given area and to determine a maximum area for a given perimeter in order to design the most cost effective rectangular pen. NOTE: The spreadsheet feature of the graphing calculator could be used instead.
investigate the relationship between surface area and volume. (Ch. 9)	MGV.01, MG1.02, MG1.03 (MGV.01, MG1.02, MG1.03) Students use the special capabilities of a spreadsheet to automatically recalculate measurements until they determine a minimum surface area for a given volume and a maximum volume for a given surface area in order to design cost effective containers. NOTE: The spreadsheet feature of the graphing calculator could be used instead.

Planning Chart and Correlation Between *MATHPOWER*™ 9, *Ontario Edition*, Student Text and the Ontario Grade 9 Academic Curriculum

NOTES:

1. Page references apply to both the student text and the *Teacher's Resource Binder* Chapter Handbooks.
2. Curriculum codes indicate that the expectation is met. Curriculum codes in parentheses indicate that the expectation is addressed in part.

Chapter 1   Connecting Numbers and Variables

MATHPOWER™ 9, Ontario Edition, Student Text	Page	Correlation to the Curriculum	Teacher's Notes (for example: date, time allotted, etc.)
1.1 Strategies for Estimation	4	review	
Investigating Math: Words to Symbols	8	review	
1.2 Variables in Expressions	10	NA1.06 NA4.01	
1.3 Problem Solving: Sequence the Operations	12	NA1.04, NA1.05, NA1.06	
1.4 Exponents, Powers, and Variables	14	NA1.04 NA2.01	
1.5 The Exponent Rules	17	NA2.06	
1.6 Reviewing Integers	19	review	

Planning Chart and Correlation Between *MATHPOWER™ 9, Ontario Edition*, Student Text and the Ontario Grade 9 Academic Curriculum

Chapter 1   [Continued]

MATHPOWER™ 9, Ontario Edition, Student Text	Page	Correlation to the Curriculum	Teacher's Notes (for example: date, time allotted, etc.)
Technology: Sorting Networks	25	(RE1.02, RE1.04)	
1.7 Powers With Integral Bases	26	NA1.04, NA1.06 NA2.01, NA2.06	
1.8 Problem Solving: Look for a Pattern	30	NA1.05 NA4.01	
1.9 Order of Operations: Whole Numbers, Decimals, and Integers	32	review	
1.10 Expressions With Integers	36	NA2.01	
1.11 Problem Solving: Use a Data Bank	38	NA1.05 (RE1.03)	
Computer Data Bank: Using the Databases	41	NA1.03 RE1.03, RE1.04	
1.12 Modelling Math— Astronomy: How Can We Model Distances in the Solar System?	42		

Notes

_____

_____

_____

_____

Planning Chart and Correlation Between *MATHPOWER*™ 9, *Ontario Edition*, Student Text and the Ontario Grade 9 Academic Curriculum

NOTES:

1. Page references apply to both the student text and the *Teacher's Resource Binder* Chapter Handbooks.
2. Curriculum codes indicate that the expectation is met. Curriculum codes in parentheses indicate that the expectation is addressed in part.

Chapter 2   Ratio, Rate, and Percent

MATHPOWER™ 9, Ontario Edition, Student Text	Page	Correlation to the Curriculum	Teacher's Notes (for example: date, time allotted, etc.)
2.1 Ratios	52	review	
2.2 Problem Solving: Solve a Simpler Problem	56	NA1.05 NA4.01	
Investigating Math: Equations	58	NA3.04	
2.3 Equivalent Ratios and Proportions	60	review	
2.4 Rates and Units Pricing	65	review	
2.5 Problem Solving: Make Assumptions	70	NA1.03, NA1.05	
2.6 Percent	72	review	
2.7 Ratios, Fractions, and Decimals as Percents	74	review	

Chapter 2   [Continued]

MATHPOWER™ 9, Ontario Edition, Student Text	Page	Correlation to the Curriculum	Teacher's Notes (for example: date, time allotted, etc.)
2.8 Using Percents	79	NA1.03, NA1.04, NA1.06	
2.9 Problem Solving: Use Logic	86	NA1.05	
Technology: Solving Problems Using Spreadsheets	88	RE1.04	
Technology: Electronic Spreadsheets in Sports	89	RE1.04	
2.10 Modelling Math — The Environment: How Can We Model the Population and Distribution of Wildlife Species?	90		

Notes

_____

_____

_____

_____

_____

_____

Planning Chart and Correlation Between *MATHPOWER*™ 9, *Ontario Edition*, Student Text and the Ontario Grade 9 Academic Curriculum

NOTES:
1. Page references apply to both the student text and the *Teacher's Resource Binder* Chapter Handbooks.
2. Curriculum codes indicate that the expectation is met. Curriculum codes in parentheses indicate that the expectation is addressed in part.

Chapter 3   Real Numbers

MATHPOWER™ 9, Ontario Edition, Student Text	Page	Correlation to the Curriculum	Teacher's Notes (for example: date, time allotted, etc.)
Investigating Math: Mental Math—Powers of Ten	100	review	
3.1 Scientific Notation— Large Numbers	102	NA1.04 NA2.04, NA2.05	
Technology: Calculators and Repeating Decimals	104	(NA1.02), NA1.04	
Investigating Math: Writing Decimals as Fractions	105	(NA1.02)	
Technology: Exploring Zero and Negative Exponents	106	(NA2.03)	
3.2 Zero and Negative Exponents	108	NA1.04 NA2.03, NA2.06	
3.3 Scientific Notation — Small Numbers	113	NA1.04 NA2.04, NA2.05	
3.4 Problem Solving: Guess and Check	116	NA1.05	
3.5 Rational Numbers	118	(NA1.01), NA1.04	
Investigating Math: Canada's Musical Place Names	124	review	
3.6 Multiplying Rational Numbers	126	NA1.01, NA1.04, NA1.06 NA2.01	

Planning Chart and Correlation Between *MATHPOWER*™ 9, *Ontario Edition*, Student Text and the Ontario Grade 9 Academic Curriculum

Chapter 3   [Continued]

MATHPOWER™ 9, Ontario Edition, Student Text	Page	Correlation to the Curriculum	Teacher's Notes (for example: date, time allotted, etc.)
3.7 Dividing Rational Numbers	130	NA1.01, NA1.04, NA1.06	
3.8 Problem Solving: Use a Diagram	134	NA1.05 NA4.03	
3.9 Adding and Subtracting Rational Numbers	136	NA1.01, NA1.04, NA1.06	
Technology: Budgets From a Spreadsheet	139	RE1.04	
3.10 Order of Operations With Rational Numbers	140	NA1.01, NA1.04 NA2.01	
Computer Data Bank: Box Office Hits	143	NA1.03 RE1.03, RE1.04	
3.11 Problem Solving: Solve Fermi Problems	144	NA1.05 RE1.03	
3.12 Square Roots	146	NA1.02, NA1.04, NA1.06	
3.13 Applying Formulas	152	NA1.04, NA1.06 NA4.01	
3.14 Modelling Math— Transportation: How Can We Model Driving Routes?	154	NA1.03	

Notes

_____

_____

_____

_____

_____

_____

Planning Chart and Correlation Between *MATHPOWER*™ 9, *Ontario Edition*, Student Text and the Ontario Grade 9 Academic Curriculum

NOTES:
1. Page references apply to both the student text and the *Teacher's Resource Binder* Chapter Handbooks.
2. Curriculum codes indicate that the expectation is met. Curriculum codes in parentheses indicate that the expectation is addressed in part.

Chapter 4   Statistics

MATHPOWER™ 9, Ontario Edition, Student Text	Page	Correlation to the Curriculum	Teacher's Notes (for example: date, time allotted, etc.)
4.1 Hypotheses, Surveys, and Inferences	164	(RE1.01, RE1.02), RE1.03, RE1.04, RE1.05	
Technology: Graphing Calculators and Random Sampling	168	(RE1.02)	
4.2 Sampling Techniques	169	(RE1.02)	
4.3 Bias	176	(RE1.02)	
4.4 Problem Solving: Work Backward	180	NA1.03, NA1.04, NA1.05	
4.5 Mean, Median, Mode, and Range	182	RE1.03, RE1.04	
Investigating Math: Histograms	188	RE1.03, RE1.04, RE1.05	
Technology: Graphics Software Packages	190	RE1.04	
4.6 Stem-and-Leaf Plots	192	RE1.03, RE1.04, RE1.05	
4.7 Box-and-Whisker Plots and Percentiles	195	RE1.03, RE1.04	
4.8 Broken-Line Graphs	199	RE1.03, RE1.04, RE1.05	
4.9 Problem Solving: Interpret Graphs	202	RE3.02	
4.10 Scatter Plots	204	RE1.03, RE1.04, RE1.05 RE2.02, RE3.01	
4.11 Lines of Best Fit	209	RE1.03, RE1.04, RE1.05, RE1.06, RE2.02 RE3.01	

Planning Chart and Correlation Between *MATHPOWER*™ *9*, *Ontario Edition*, Student Text and the Ontario Grade 9 Academic Curriculum

Chapter 4   [Continued]

MATHPOWER™ *9, Ontario Edition*, Student Text	Page	Correlation to the Curriculum	Teacher's Notes (for example: date, time allotted, etc.)
Technology: Scatter Plots and Computer Spreadsheets	212	RE1.01, RE1.03, RE1.04, RE1.05, RE2.02, RE3.01	
Investigating Math: Scientific Data and the Line of Best Fit	214	RE1.01, RE1.03, RE1.04, RE1.05, RE2.02 RE3.01	
Technology: Internet Experiment	215	(RE1.01, RE1.02), RE1.03, RE1.04, RE1.05, RE1.06, RE1.07	
4.12 Determining Relationships	216	RE1.01, RE1.02, RE1.03, RE1.04, RE1.05, RE1.06, RE1.07	
Technology: Collecting Voltage Data Using CBL™	218	RE1.03, RE1.04, RE1.06	
Technology: Collecting Jump-Height Data Using CBL™	219	RE1.03, RE1.04, RE1.06	
Technology: Collecting Rebound-Height Data Using CBR™ or CBL™	220	RE1.03, RE1.04	
Technology: Collecting Distance and Time Data Using CBR™ or CBL™	221	RE1.01, RE1.03, RE1.04 RE2.02 RE3.04	
4.13 Problem Solving: Use a Table or a Spreadsheet	222	NA1.03, NA1.05	
Computer Data Bank: Nations of the World	225	NA1.01, NA1.03 RE1.03, RE1.04, RE1.05, RE2.02	
4.14 Modelling Math—English: How Can We Model Word Use?	226	RE1.01, RE1.03, RE1.04, RE1.05	

Notes

Planning Chart and Correlation Between *MATHPOWER™ 9, Ontario Edition*, Student Text and the Ontario Grade 9 Academic Curriculum

NOTES:
1. Page references apply to both the student text and the *Teacher's Resource Binder* Chapter Handbooks.
2. Curriculum codes indicate that the expectation is met. Curriculum codes in parentheses indicate that the expectation is addressed in part.

Chapter 5   Linear and Non-Linear Relations

MATHPOWER™ 9, Ontario Edition, Student Text	Page	Correlation to the Curriculum	Teacher's Notes (for example: date, time allotted, etc.)
Investigating Math: Relationships in Polygons	238	NA4.01 RE1.03, RE1.04, RE1.05, RE1.07	
5.1 Relations as Ordered Pairs	240	NA4.01 RE1.04, RE1.05 RE2.01	
5.2 Graphing Ordered Pairs	246	AG3.01, AG3.02	
5.3 Graphing Linear Relations	250	AG3.01, AG3.02, AG3.03 RE3.01	
5.4 Graphing Linear Equations	254	AG3.01, AG3.02, AG3.03, AG3.04 RE2.01 RE3.01	
5.5 Direct and Partial Variation	259	NA4.01, NA4.02 RE2.01 RE3.01, RE3.04 AG3.01, AG3.02, AG3.03	
Technology: Finding the Equation of a Line	268	AG3.03, AG3.04	
5.6 Equations of Lines of Best Fit	269	RE1.03, RE1.04, RE1.05, RE1.07 RE2.02, RE2.03 RE3.01 AG3.02, AG3.03	

Planning Chart and Correlation Between *MATHPOWER*™ *9, Ontario Edition*, Student Text and the Ontario Grade 9 Academic Curriculum

Chapter 5 [Continued]

MATHPOWER™ *9, Ontario Edition*, Student Text	Page	Correlation to the Curriculum	Teacher's Notes (for example: date, time allotted, etc.)
5.7 Non-Linear Relations	275	RE1.03, RE1.04 RE2.05	
Investigating Math: Finite Differences	280	RE2.06 RE3.03 AG3.02	
5.8 General Relations	282	RE2.04 RE3.02	
Computer Data Bank: Summer Olympics	287	NA1.01 RE1.03, RE1.04, RE1.05, RE2.02	
5.9 Modelling Math— Sports: How Can We Model the Flight of an Object?	288		

Notes

_____

_____

_____

_____

_____

_____

_____

Planning Chart and Correlation Between *MATHPOWER*™ *9, Ontario Edition,* Student Text and the Ontario Grade 9 Academic Curriculum

NOTES:
1. Page references apply to both the student text and the *Teacher's Resource Binder* Chapter Handbooks.
2. Curriculum codes indicate that the expectation is met. Curriculum codes in parentheses indicate that the expectation is addressed in part.

Chapter 6 Algebra

MATHPOWER™ *9, Ontario Edition,* Student Text	Page	Correlation to the Curriculum	Teacher's Notes (for example: date, time allotted, etc.)
6.1 Collecting Like Terms	298	(NA2.02, NA3.01)	
Investigating Math: Modelling With Algebra Tiles	302	(NA2.02)	
6.2 Polynomials	304	MG2.01	
6.3 Adding Polynomials	307	(NA2.02) NA3.01	
6.4 Subtracting Polynomials	310	(NA2.02) NA3.01	
6.5 The Distributive Property	313	(NA2.02) NA3.03	
6.6 Multiplying Monomials by Monomials	316	(NA2.02), NA2.06	
6.7 Powers of Monomials	318	(NA2.02), NA2.06 MG2.01	

Planning Chart and Correlation Between *MATHPOWER™ 9, Ontario Edition*, Student Text and the Ontario Grade 9 Academic Curriculum

Chapter 6   [Continued]

MATHPOWER™ 9, Ontario Edition, Student Text	Page	Correlation to the Curriculum	Teacher's Notes (for example: date, time allotted, etc.)
6.8 Multiplying a Polynomial by a Monomial	321	NA2.06 NA3.02, NA3.03	
6.9 Dividing Monomials by Monomials	323	NA2.06	
6.10 Common Factors and the GCF	326	(NA3.02)	
6.11 Factoring Expressions With Common Factors	328	(NA2.02) NA3.02	
Technology: Polynomials and the Graphing Calculators	330	(NA2.02) NA3.01, NA3.02, NA3.03	
6.12 Modelling Math — English How Can We Model Readability?	331	NA1.01, NA1.04	

Notes

_____

_____

_____

_____

_____

_____

_____

_____

_____

_____

Planning Chart and Correlation Between *MATHPOWER*™ *9, Ontario Edition*, Student Text and the Ontario Grade 9 Academic Curriculum

NOTES:
1. Page references apply to both the student text and the *Teacher's Resource Binder* Chapter Handbooks.
2. Curriculum codes indicate that the expectation is met. Curriculum codes in parentheses indicate that the expectation is addressed in part.

Chapter 7 Equations

MATHPOWER™ 9, Ontario Edition, Student Text	Page	Correlation to the Curriculum	Teacher's Notes (for example: date, time allotted, etc.)
7.1 Solving Equations Using Addition and Subtraction	342	NA1.01 NA3.04	
7.2 Solving Equations Using Division and Multiplication	346	NA1.01 NA3.04	
7.3 Solving Multi-Step Equations	350	NA1.04 NA3.04	
7.4 Solving Equations With the Variable on Both Sides	354	NA1.04 NA3.04	
7.5 Solving Equations With Brackets	356	NA1.04 NA3.04	
7.6 Solving Equations With Fractions and Decimals	359	NA1.04 NA3.04	
7.7 Writing Equations	362	(NA4.01)	
7.8 Using Equations to Solve Problems	364	NA1.01, NA1.05, NA1.06 NA3.04, NA3.05 NA4.01, NA4.02	

Planning Chart and Correlation Between *MATHPOWER*™ *9, Ontario Edition*, Student Text and the Ontario Grade 9 Academic Curriculum

Chapter 7 [Continued]

MATHPOWER™ *9, Ontario Edition*, Student Text	Page	Correlation to the Curriculum	Teacher's Notes (for example: date, time allotted, etc.)
7.9 Working With Formulas	368	NA1.01, NA1.04 NA3.04, NA3.06	
7.10 Developing Formulas	371	RE2.01	
Investigating Math: Developing Pick's Formula	374	NA4.01 RE1.04	
7.11 Uniform Motion Problems	376	NA1.01 NA3.04 NA4.01, NA4.02	
Technology: Solving Equations Using a Graphing Calculator	378	NA3.04 NA4.01	
Computer Data Bank: Healthy Eating	380	NA1.01, NA1.03 RE1.04	
7.12 Modelling Math— Criminology: How Can We Identify People?	382		

Notes

_____

_____

_____

_____

_____

_____

Planning Chart and Correlation Between *MATHPOWER*™ 9, *Ontario Edition*, Student Text and the Ontario Grade 9 Academic Curriculum

NOTES:
1. Page references apply to both the student text and the *Teacher's Resource Binder* Chapter Handbooks.
2. Curriculum codes indicate that the expectation is met. Curriculum codes in parentheses indicate that the expectation is addressed in part.

Chapter 8   Analytic Geometry

MATHPOWER™ 9, Ontario Edition, Student Text	Page	Correlation to the Curriculum	Teacher's Notes (for example: date, time allotted, etc.)
Investigating Math: Lengths of Horizontal and Vertical Line Segments	392	(AG2.01) AG3.01	
8.1 Slope	394	AG2.01, AG2.05 AG3.01, AG3.02	
Investigating Math: Finite Differences and Slopes of Linear Relations	402	AG2.01, AG2.03	
Computer Data Bank: Alpine Skiing in Canada	403	NA1.01, NA1.03 NA3.05 RE1.03, RE1.04 AG2.01	
8.2 Slope as Rate of Change	404	NA1.04, NA1.06 RE1.03 AG2.01, AG2.02 AG3.02	
Technology: Programming a Graphing Calculator	410	AG2.01, AG2.02	
Technology: Characteristics of Linear and Non-Linear Equations	411	RE2.06 AG1.01, AG1.02, AG1.03, AG1.04	
8.3 Linear Equations: Point-Slope Form	412	NA3.06 NA4.01 AG1.04 AG2.01, AG2.02 AG3.02, AG3.03, AG3.04	

Planning Chart and Correlation Between *MATHPOWER*™ 9, *Ontario Edition*, Student Text and the Ontario Grade 9 Academic Curriculum

Chapter 8   [Continued]

MATHPOWER™ 9, Ontario Edition, Student Text	Page	Correlation to the Curriculum	Teacher's Notes (for example: date, time allotted, etc.)
Technology: Graphing Calculators and the Properties of Lines	421	AG2.04, AG2.05 AG3.03	
8.4 Linear Equations: Slope and *y*-Intercept Form	424	NA3.06 AG1.03, AG1.04 AG2.01, AG2.02 AG3.02, AG3.03, AG3.04, AG3.06	
8.5 Methods for Graphing Linear Equations	430	NA3.06 NA4.01 AG1.04 AG2.01, AG2.02 AG3.02, AG3.03, AG3.04, AG3.06	
8.6 Parallel and Perpendicular Lines	434	NA3.06 NA4.01 AG1.03, AG1.04 AG2.05 AG3.02, AG3.03, AG3.04	
8.7 Intersecting Lines	439	NA4.01 AG3.02, AG3.03, AG3.08	
8.8 Modelling Math— Geography: How Can We Model Slopes on the Earth?	442	NA1.03 RE2.04 AG2.01	

Notes _____

_____

_____

_____

_____

_____

_____

_____

_____

_____

Planning Chart and Correlation Between *MATHPOWER™ 9, Ontario Edition*, Student Text and the Ontario Grade 9 Academic Curriculum

NOTES:
1. Page references apply to both the student text and the *Teacher's Resource Binder* Chapter Handbooks.
2. Curriculum codes indicate that the expectation is met. Curriculum codes in parentheses indicate that the expectation is addressed in part.

Chapter 9   Measurement

MATHPOWER™ 9, Ontario Edition, Student Text	Page	Correlation to the Curriculum	Teacher's Notes (for example: date, time allotted, etc.)
Investigating Math: Reviewing Formulas	454	NA1.01 NA2.02	
9.1 Area of Composite Figures	456	NA1.01, NA1.04 NA2.02	
Investigating Math: Optimizing Perimeter and Area	460	RE1.04, RE1.05, RE1.07 MG1.04	
Investigating Math: Surface Areas and Volumes of Right Prisms	464	NA1.01 MG2.01	
9.2 Surface Area and Volume of a Prism	466	NA1.01, NA1.04 MG2.01, MG2.02, MG2.04	
Investigating Math: Surface Area and Volume of a Cylinder	472	NA1.01, NA1.02 MG2.01	
Investigating Math: Surface Area and Volume of a Cone	474	NA1.02	
9.3 Surface Area and Volume of a Cylinder and a Cone	476	NA1.01, NA1.04 MG2.01, MG2.02, MG2.04	

Planning Chart and Correlation Between *MATHPOWER*™ 9, *Ontario Edition*, Student Text and the Ontario Grade 9 Academic Curriculum

Chapter 9 [Continued]

MATHPOWER™ 9, Ontario Edition, Student Text	Page	Correlation to the Curriculum	Teacher's Notes (for example: date, time allotted, etc.)
Investigating Math: Varying the Dimensions of Prisms and Cylinders	481	NA1.01, NA1.02 RE1.03, RE1.04, RE1.06 MG1.01	
Investigating Math: Surface Area and Volume of a Regular Pyramid	484	NA1.01 MG2.01	
Investigating Math: Surface Area and Volume of a Sphere	486	NA1.01 MG2.01	
9.4 Surface Area and Volume of a Pyramid and a Sphere	488	NA1.01, NA1.02, NA1.04 MG2.01, MG2.02, MG2.04	
Technology: Design Problems in Three Dimensions	494	RE1.05, RE1.06 MG1.02, MG1.03	
Technology: Graphing Calculator Programs for Surface Area and Volume	498	MG2.01	
9.5 Volume, Capacity, and Mass	499	(MG2.01)	
9.6 Modelling Math — Cartography: How Can We Model the Earth in Two Dimensions?	501	(MG2.01)	

Notes

_____

_____

_____

Planning Chart and Correlation Between *MATHPOWER*™ 9, *Ontario Edition*, Student Text and the Ontario Grade 9 Academic Curriculum

NOTES:
1. Page references apply to both the student text and the *Teacher's Resource Binder* Chapter Handbooks.
2. Curriculum codes indicate that the expectation is met. Curriculum codes in parentheses indicate that the expectation is addressed in part.

Chapter 10   Geometry

MATHPOWER™ 9, Ontario Edition, Student Text	Page	Correlation to the Curriculum	Teacher's Notes (for example: date, time allotted, etc.)
Investigating Math: Angles, Intersecting Lines, and Triangles	512	NA1.01	
Technology: Exploring Interior and Exterior Angles Using Geometry Software	515	MG3.01	
Investigating Math: Exploring Interior and Exterior Angles	518	MG3.01	
10.1 Interior and Exterior Angles of Triangles and Quadrilaterals	520	NA1.01 NA3.04 MG3.01	
Technology: Exploring Angle Bisectors, Medians, and Altitudes Using Geometry Software	525	MG3.02, MG3.04	
Investigating Math: Geometric Constructions	527	(MG3.02)	
Investigating Math: Exploring Angle Bisectors, Medians, and Altitudes	529	MG3.02, MG3.04	
Technology: Exploring Angles and Parallel Lines Using Geometry Software	530	MG3.01	

Planning Chart and Correlation Between *MATHPOWER*™ *9*, *Ontario Edition*, Student Text and the Ontario Grade 9 Academic Curriculum

Chapter 10 [Continued]

MATHPOWER™ 9, Ontario Edition, Student Text	Page	Correlation to the Curriculum	Teacher's Notes (for example: date, time allotted, etc.)
10.2 Angles and Parallel Lines	532	NA1.01 NA3.04 MG3.01	
Investigating Math: Polygons	537	MG3.03	
Technology: Exploring the Sides and Diagonals of Polygons Using Geometry Software	540	MG3.03, MG3.04	
Investigating Math: Exploring Sides and Diagonals of Polygons	544	MG3.03, MG3.04	
Investigating Math: Posing Questions and Testing Conjectures	550	MG3.04	
10.3 Analyzing Conjectures Using Examples and Counterexamples	552	MG3.05	
10.4 Modelling Math—Biology: How Can We Model Your Field of Vision?	555	RE1.03, RE1.04, RE1.06, RE1.07	

Notes

_____

_____

_____

_____

_____

_____

_____

Teacher Resource Master 1 *1-cm grid paper*

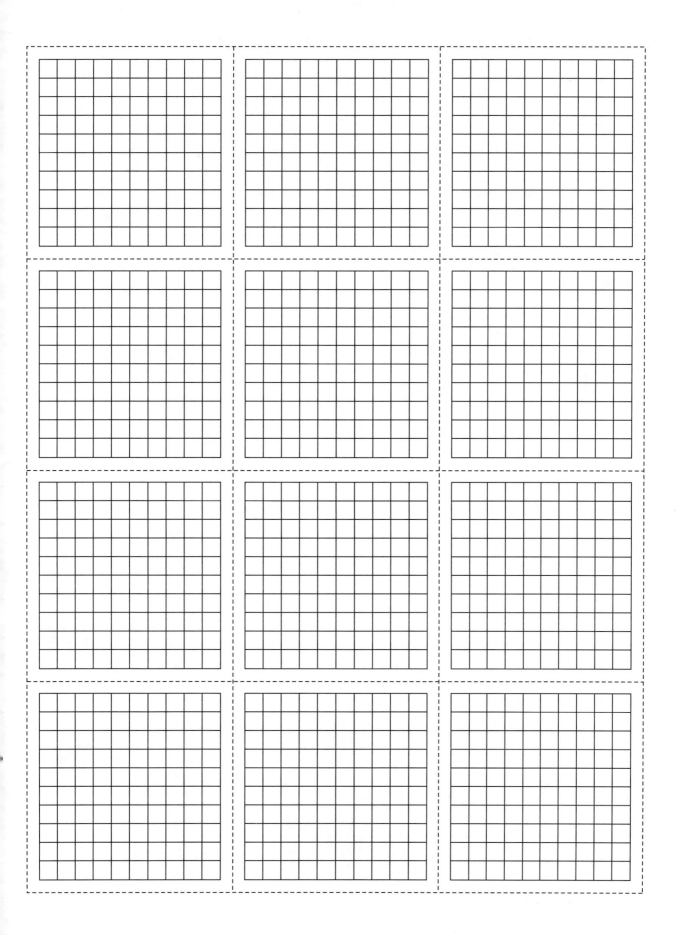

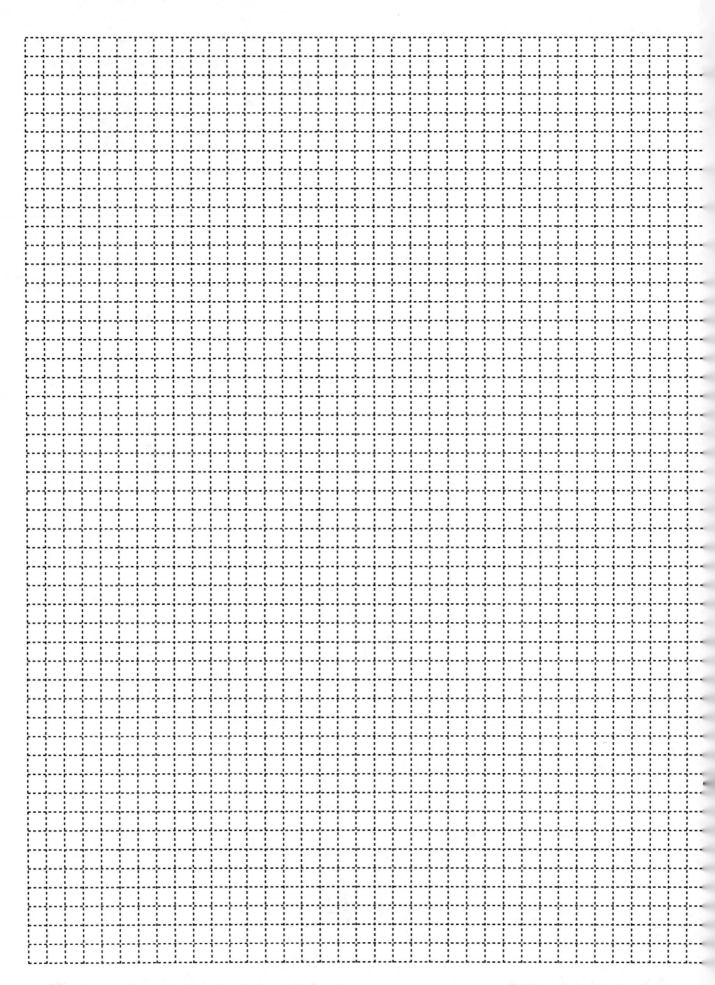

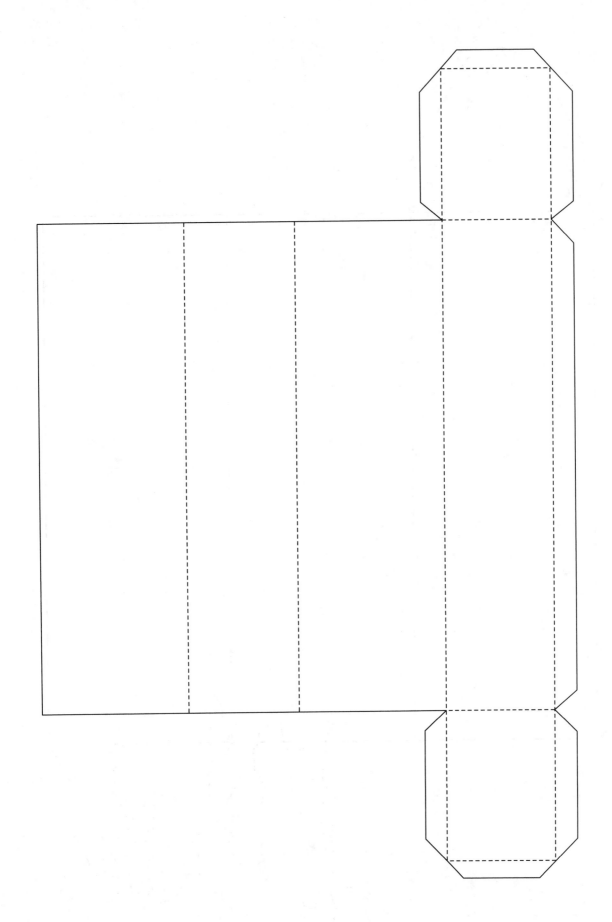

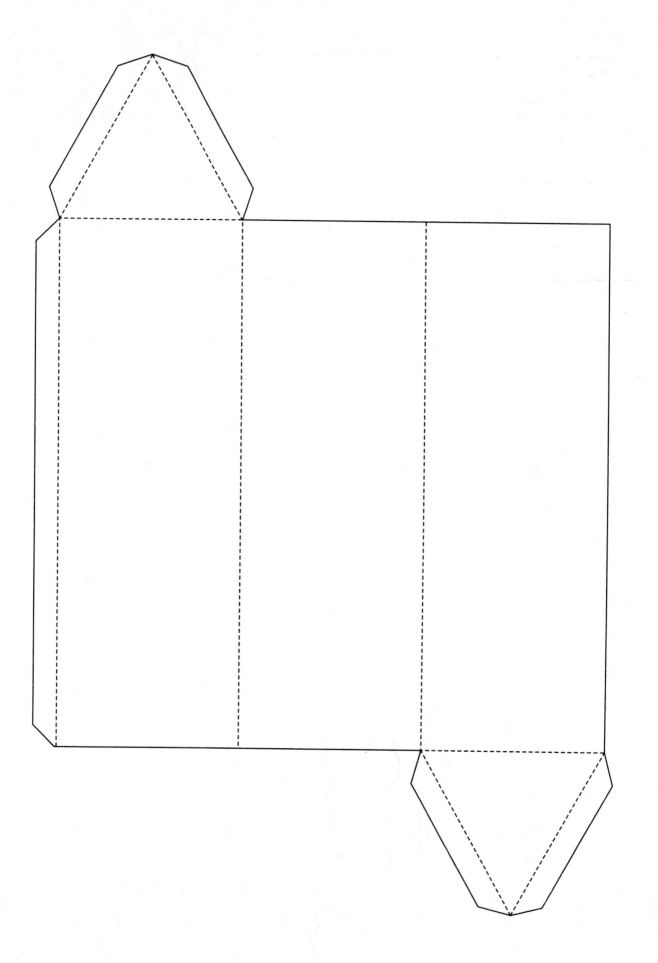

Notes

Notes

Notes

Notes

Credits

Quotations on pages 2, 4, 5, 10, 12, 16, and 19: © Queen's Printer for Ontario, 1999. Reproduced with permission

Quotation on page 7: NCTM *Principles and Standards of School Mathematics: Discussion Draft*, October 1998

Quotation on page 10: NCTM *Mathematical Modeling in the Secondary School Curriculum*, 1991

MATHPOWER™ 9, Ontario Edition
Additional Support for Your Classroom

Blackline Masters

ISBN 0-07-560798-0

THE ULTIMATE IN CLASSROOM-READY CONVENIENCE (272 pages)

Includes: Tips for Learning Math
Rich Learning Activities (8) with accompanying student exemplars and scoring rubrics
Chapters 1–10 Practice: A Blackline Master for each numbered section
A Self-Check, with references to the teaching examples in the student text
Test 1 — "B" level; Test 2 — "C" level
Answers

Computer Data Bank

ISBN 0-07-560799-9

Students will work with 5 databases of real-world information as they find, organize, and sort data; perform calculations; display data in tables and lists; summarize data; and create graphs.

- Can be used with any one of five database applications:
  ClarisWorks 4.0 and 5.0, Windows® 95; ClarisWorks 4.0 and 5.0, Macintosh OS 7.0; Corel Paradox 8, Windows® 95; Microsoft Works 4.0, Windows® 95; Microsoft Access 97, Windows® 95
- Teacher's Resource contains *Getting Started* Blackline Masters that provide students with all they need to know about the specific database application to carry out the activities. No need to teach the application software.

Computerized Assessment Bank (Windows)

ISBN 0-07-560800-6

- Vinyl holder with User's Notes and CD-ROM
- Allows teachers:
  ▶ to quickly create and print tests, complete with graphics, charts, and diagrams
  ▶ to create and add their own questions
  ▶ to choose questions by chapter, numbered section, or curriculum expectation
- Algorithm and static questions
- Multiple choice and free response questions

Solutions

ISBN 0-07-560801-4

COMPLETE MODEL SOLUTIONS FOR:
- Every odd-numbered question in the Practice sections
- All other questions (Applications and Problem Solving, Power problems, Review, Exploring Math, Chapter Check, Problem Solving: Using the Strategies, Cumulative Review)
- Approximately 800 pages

McGraw-Hill Ryerson

Toronto Montréal New York Burr Ridge Bogotá Caracas Lisbon London Madrid
Mexico City Milan New Delhi Seoul Singapore Sydney Taipei

MATHPOWER™ 9
ONTARIO EDITION

Teacher's Resource Binder

Contributing Writers

Jacqueline Williams
Oakville, Ontario

Shirley Barrett
Richmond Hill, Ontario

Janice Nixon
Toronto, Ontario

Christine Suurtamm
Mississauga, Ontario

Tess Miller
Whitby, Ontario

Paul Zolis
Scarborough, Ontario

Technology Consultant

Fred Ferneyhough
Brampton, Ontario

MATHPOWER™ Series, Grades 9–12

Explore our
Web Site
http://www.mcgrawhill.ca

McGraw-Hill Ryerson Limited
A Subsidiary of The McGraw-Hill Companies

ISBN 0-07-086335-0

9 780070 863354